Keep your finger on the KS1 Maths pulse!

Pupils certainly need lots of practice to harvest all the skills for
Year 2 Maths. That's where this super CGP book comes in...

With a bountiful supply of activities to build skills from the Year 2
curriculum, it's got every day of the autumn term done and dusted.

And what's more, the colourful pictures are ideal for making sure pupils stay
interested. Ideal for in class, at home, on a farm... the sky's the limit!

What CGP is all about

Our sole aim here at CGP is to produce the highest quality books
— carefully written, immaculately presented and
dangerously close to being funny.

Then we work our socks off to get them out to you
— at the cheapest possible prices.

Contents

☑ Use the tick boxes to help keep a record of which tests have been attempted.

Published by CGP

ISBN: 978 1 78908 507 5

Editors: Eleanor Crabtree, Josie Gilbert, Duncan Lindsay, Sarah Pattison, Sarah Williams

With thanks to Sharon Gulliver and Glenn Rogers for the proofreading.

With thanks to Jan Greenway for the copyright research.

Cover and Graphics used throughout the book © www.edu-clips.com
Clipart from Corel®

£1 coin © iStock.com/ LPETTET
50 pence coin © iStock.com/duncan1890
20 pence coin © iStock.com/Jaap2
10 pence coin © iStock.com/john shepherd
5 pence coin © iStock.com/duncan1890
2 pence coin © iStock.com/peterspiro
1 pence coin © iStock.com/coopder1

Printed by Elanders Ltd, Newcastle upon Tyne.
Based on the classic CGP style created by Richard Parsons.

How to Use this Book

- This book contains <u>60 daily practice tests</u>.

- We've split them into <u>12 sections</u> — that's roughly one for <u>each week</u> of the Year 2 <u>Autumn term</u>.

- Each week is made up of <u>5 tests</u>, so there's one for <u>every school day</u> of the term (Monday – Friday).

- Each test should take about <u>10 minutes</u> to complete.

- The tests contain a <u>mix</u> of topics from <u>Year 1</u> and <u>Year 2</u>. <u>New Year 2 topics</u> are gradually introduced as you go through the book.

- The tests <u>increase in difficulty</u> as you progress through the term.

- Each test looks something like this:

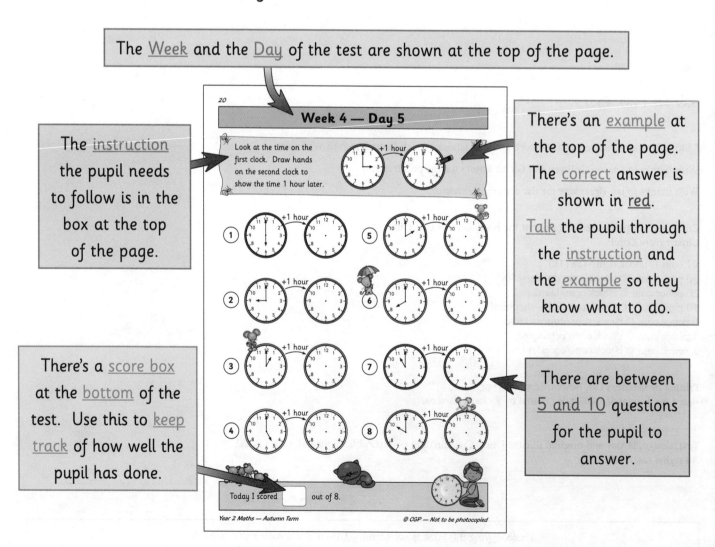

The <u>Week</u> and the <u>Day</u> of the test are shown at the top of the page.

The <u>instruction</u> the pupil needs to follow is in the box at the top of the page.

There's an <u>example</u> at the top of the page. The <u>correct</u> answer is shown in <u>red</u>. <u>Talk</u> the pupil through the <u>instruction</u> and the <u>example</u> so they know what to do.

There's a <u>score box</u> at the <u>bottom</u> of the test. Use this to <u>keep track</u> of how well the pupil has done.

There are between <u>5 and 10</u> questions for the pupil to answer.

Week 1 — Day 1

Circle the tallest object.

castle   ball   goat

(1) tree   beetle   spade

(2) muffin   hammer   crane

(3) brush   elephant   paint tin

(4) bird   goat   house

(5) cup   tent   cake

(6) wardrobe   grapes   worm

(7) radish   tree   fish

(8) guitar   cup   bowl

(9) apple   suitcase   ant

(10) pencil   orange   rabbit

Today I scored ☐ out of 10.

    Year 2 Maths — Autumn Term

Week 1 — Day 2

Complete the sentence.

12 add 4 equals │ 16 │

(1) 5 add 7 equals [ ]

(2) 9 subtract 3 equals [ ]

(3) 11 subtract 1 equals [ ]

(4) 7 add 12 equals [ ]

(5) 8 add 8 equals [ ]

(6) 16 add 4 equals [ ]

(7) 19 subtract 8 equals [ ]

(8) 15 subtract 6 equals [ ]

Today I scored [ ] out of 8.

Week 1 — Day 3

Fill in the answers.
Use the pictures
to help you.

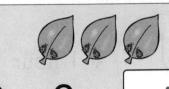

$3 \times 2 = $ 6

1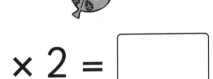

$1 \times 2 = $

5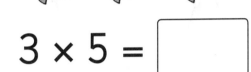

$3 \times 5 = $

2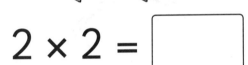

$2 \times 2 = $

6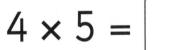

$4 \times 5 = $

3

$2 \times 5 = $

7

$6 \times 2 = $

4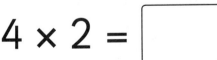

$4 \times 2 = $

8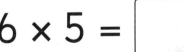

$6 \times 5 = $

Today I scored ☐ out of 8.

Year 2 Maths — Autumn Term

Week 1 — Day 4

Look at the clock. Write what the time will be one hour later.

+ 1 hour

eight o'clock

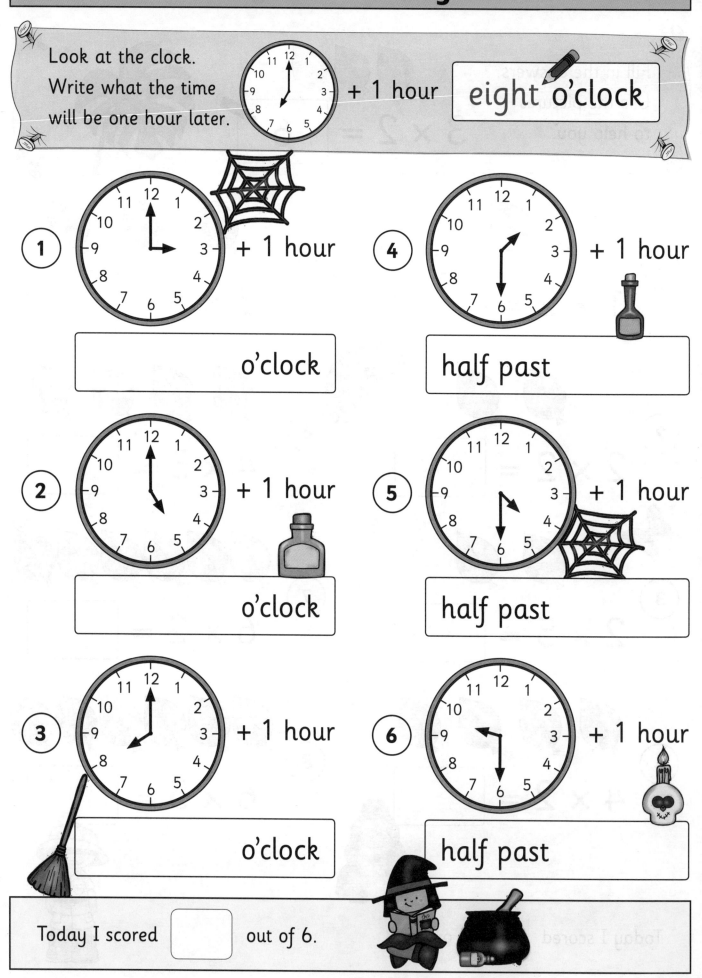

(1) + 1 hour

o'clock

(2) + 1 hour

o'clock

(3) + 1 hour

o'clock

(4) + 1 hour

half past

(5) + 1 hour

half past

(6) + 1 hour

half past

Today I scored ____ out of 6.

Week 1 — Day 5

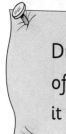

Draw the position of the pointer after it makes the turn.

quarter turn clockwise

1 half turn clockwise

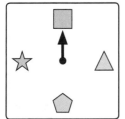 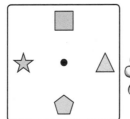

2 half turn clockwise

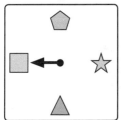 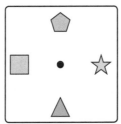

3 quarter turn clockwise

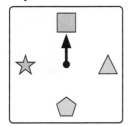 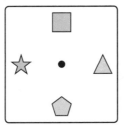

4 half turn anticlockwise

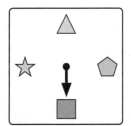 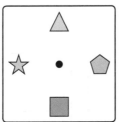

5 half turn clockwise

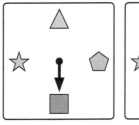 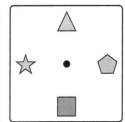

6 half turn anticlockwise

 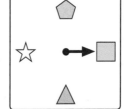 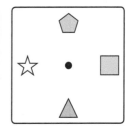

7 quarter turn anticlockwise

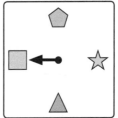 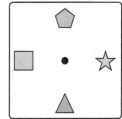

8 three-quarter turn clockwise

Today I scored ☐ out of 8.

Week 2 — Day 1

Write the name of the shape there is most of.

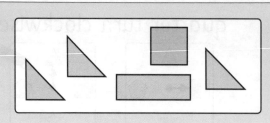

triangle

①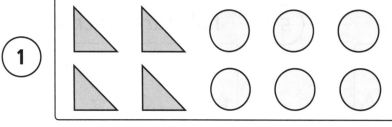

②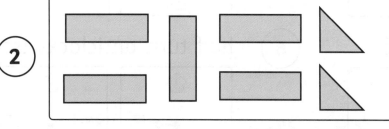

③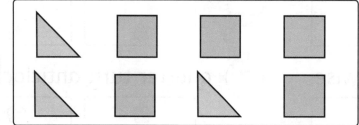

④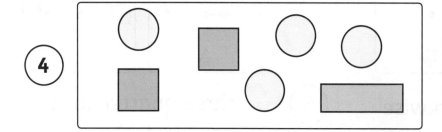

⑤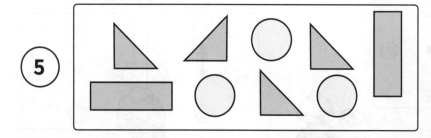

Today I scored ☐ out of 5.

Week 2 — Day 2

Circle the shape with the correct amount shaded.

one half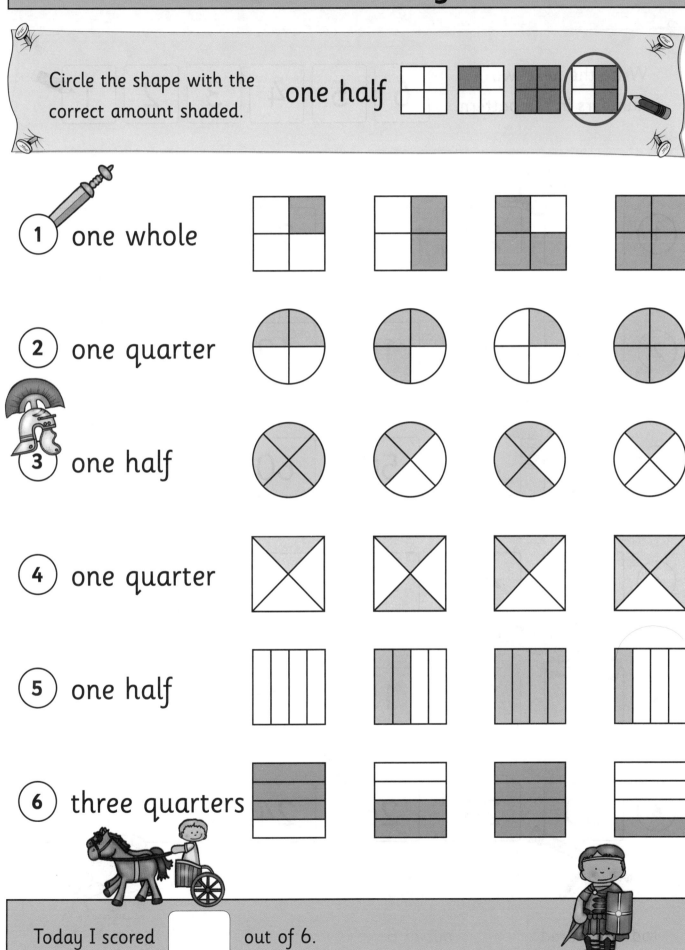

1) one whole

2) one quarter

3) one half

4) one quarter

5) one half

6) three quarters

Today I scored ☐ out of 6.

Year 2 Maths — Autumn Term

Week 2 — Day 3

Write the next two numbers in the pattern.

6	5	4	3	2	1

1) | 22 | 23 | 24 | 25 | | |
|---|---|---|---|---|---|

2) | 6 | 8 | 10 | 12 | | |
|---|---|---|---|---|---|

3) | 30 | 40 | 50 | 60 | | |
|---|---|---|---|---|---|

4) | 45 | 44 | 43 | 42 | | |
|---|---|---|---|---|---|

5) | 5 | 10 | 15 | 20 | | |
|---|---|---|---|---|---|

6) | 30 | 28 | 26 | 24 | | |
|---|---|---|---|---|---|

Today I scored [   ] out of 6.

Week 2 — Day 4

Tick the correct calculation.

$3 + 7 = 10$ ✓

$8 + 4 = 10$ ☐

(1) $6 + 5 = 11$ ☐

$6 - 5 = 11$ ☐

(2) $9 + 2 = 7$ ☐

$9 - 2 = 7$ ☐

(3) $5 + 3 = 8$ ☐

$8 + 3 = 5$ ☐

(4) $7 - 0 = 7$ ☐

$10 - 7 = 7$ ☐

(5) $10 - 4 = 8$ ☐

$13 - 5 = 8$ ☐

(6) $13 - 7 = 18$ ☐

$13 + 5 = 18$ ☐

(7) $11 + 0 = 0$ ☐

$11 - 0 = 11$ ☐

(8) $15 + 3 = 17$ ☐

$15 - 3 = 12$ ☐

(9) $12 - 3 = 9$ ☐

$14 - 6 = 9$ ☐

(10) $17 - 9 = 8$ ☐

$9 - 7 = 1$ ☐

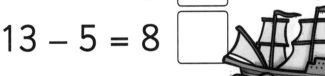

Today I scored ☐ out of 10.

Year 2 Maths — Autumn Term

Week 2 — Day 5

Share the acorns equally between the number of squirrels. Write how many acorns each squirrel gets.

2 squirrels

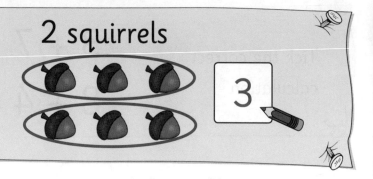

3

(1) **2 squirrels**

(5) **4 squirrels**

(2) **4 squirrels**

(6) **2 squirrels**

(3) **2 squirrels**

(7) **5 squirrels**

(4) **4 squirrels**

(8) **5 squirrels**

Today I scored [ ] out of 8.

Year 2 Maths — Autumn Term

Week 3 — Day 1

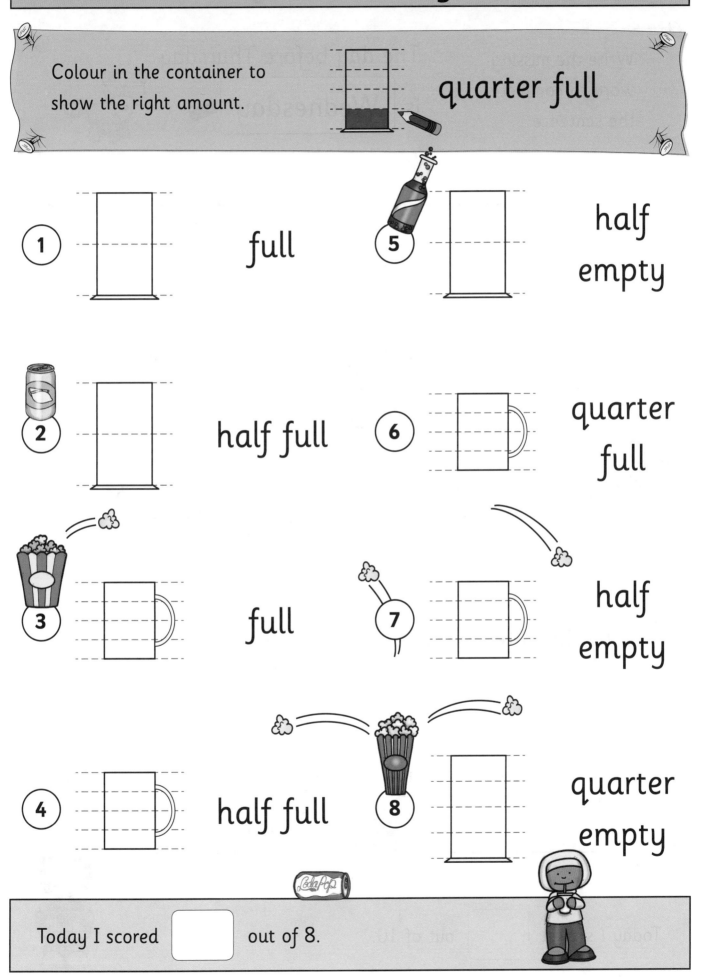

Colour in the container to show the right amount.

quarter full

1   full

5   half empty

2   half full

6   quarter full

3   full

7   half empty

4   half full

8   quarter empty

Today I scored [ ] out of 8.

Year 2 Maths — Autumn Term

Week 3 — Day 2

Write the missing word to complete the sentence.

The day before Thursday

is **Wednesday**

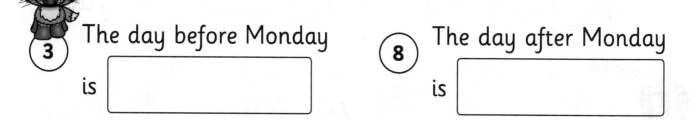

(1) The day after Wednesday

is [ ]

(6) The day before Sunday

is [ ]

(2) The day after Thursday

is [ ]

(7) The day after Friday

is [ ]

(3) The day before Monday

is [ ]

(8) The day after Monday

is [ ]

(4) The day after Saturday

is [ ]

(9) The day before Friday

is [ ]

(5) The day after Tuesday

is [ ]

(10) The day before Tuesday

is [ ]

Today I scored [ ] out of 10.

Week 3 — Day 3

Do the coins have a total value of more than 10p? Tick the right box.

yes ☐ no ☑ ✓

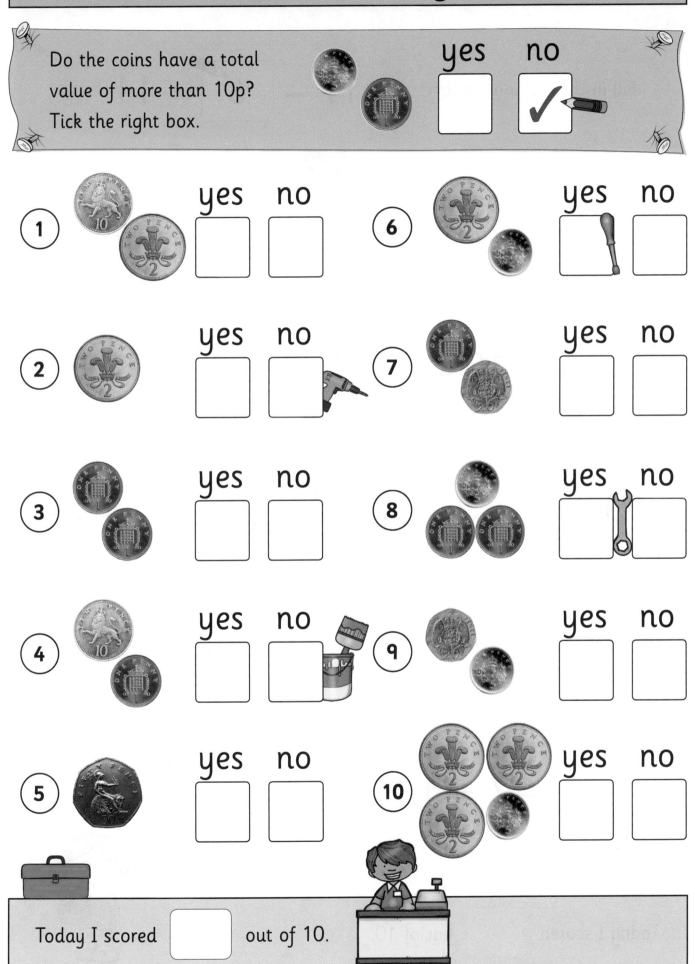

1 yes ☐ no ☐

2 yes ☐ no ☐

3 yes ☐ no ☐

4 yes ☐ no ☐

5 yes ☐ no ☐

6 yes ☐ no ☐

7 yes ☐ no ☐

8 yes ☐ no ☐

9 yes ☐ no ☐

10 yes ☐ no ☐

Today I scored ☐ out of 10.

Year 2 Maths — Autumn Term

Week 3 — Day 4

Fill in the missing number. $17 - \boxed{6} = 11$

(1) $10 - \boxed{} = 5$ (6) $\boxed{} + 5 = 14$

(2) $\boxed{} + 10 = 12$ (7) $0 = \boxed{} - 13$

(3) $12 - \boxed{} = 6$ (8) $20 - \boxed{} = 9$

(4) $11 + \boxed{} = 15$ (9) $17 = \boxed{} + 11$

(5) $\boxed{} - 7 = 10$ (10) $3 = \boxed{} - 16$

Today I scored $\boxed{}$ out of 10.

Week 3 — Day 5

Each child needs two stick arms for each snowman they build. How many sticks does the child need for their snowmen?

Anne builds 4 snowmen.

8

(1) Brad builds 1 snowman.

(5) Farid builds 7 snowmen.

(2) Cindy builds 3 snowmen.

(6) Gita builds 8 snowmen.

(3) Drew builds 5 snowmen.

(7) Juan builds 10 snowmen.

(4) Erikah builds 2 snowmen.

(8) Ian builds 9 snowmen.

Today I scored [ ] out of 8.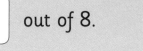

Year 2 Maths — Autumn Term

Week 4 — Day 1

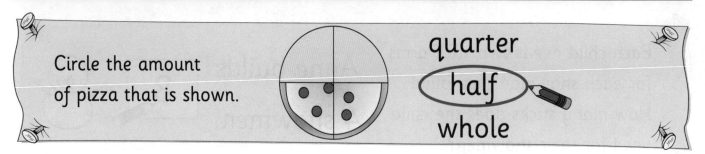

Circle the amount of pizza that is shown.

quarter

~~half~~

whole

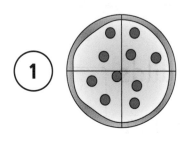

1

quarter

half

whole

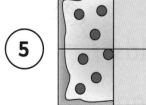

5

quarter

half

whole

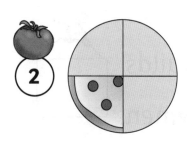

2

quarter

half

whole

6

quarter

half

whole

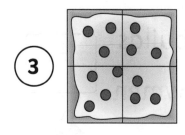

3

quarter

half

whole

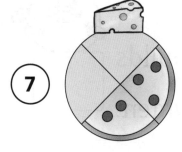

7

quarter

half

whole

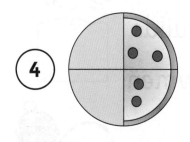

4

quarter

half

whole

8

quarter

half

whole

Today I scored ☐ out of 8.

Week 4 — Day 2

Write the number that is being described.

It has a 3 in the tens place and a 2 in the ones place.

32

1. It has a 1 in the tens place and a 5 in the ones place.

2. It has a 2 in the tens place and a 2 in the ones place.

3. It has a 3 in the tens place and a 6 in the ones place.

4. It has a 7 in the tens place and a 1 in the ones place.

5. It has a 5 in the tens place and a 9 in the ones place.

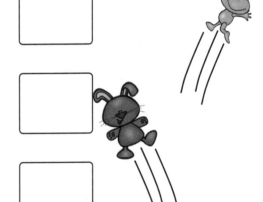

6. It has an 8 in the tens place and a 7 in the ones place.

7. It has a 9 in the tens place and a 2 in the ones place.

8. It has a 6 in the tens place and a 0 in the ones place.

Today I scored [ ] out of 8.

Week 4 — Day 3

Look at the numbers in the boxes. Write the largest number in words.

| 12 | 56 | 78 |

seventy-eight

1 | 10 | 5 | 9 |

2 | 2 | 6 | 40 |

3 | 8 | 42 | 34 |

4 | 11 | 16 | 13 |

5 | 20 | 60 | 80 |

6 | 25 | 50 | 37 |

7 | 21 | 65 | 49 |

8 | 31 | 15 | 28 |

9 | 99 | 67 | 88 |

10 | 57 | 78 | 87 |

Today I scored ☐ out of 10.

Week 4 — Day 4

Make the number sentence correct by writing <, > or = in the box.

43 **>** 35

(1) 1 ☐ 11

(6) 55 ☐ 65

(2) 19 ☐ 19

(7) 39 ☐ 33

(3) 28 ☐ 17

(8) 47 ☐ 64

(4) 50 ☐ 50

(9) 81 ☐ 84

(5) 23 ☐ 32

(10) 98 ☐ 89

Today I scored ☐ out of 10.

Year 2 Maths — Autumn Term

Week 4 — Day 5

Look at the time on the
first clock. Draw hands
on the second clock to
show the time 1 hour later.

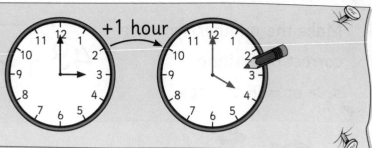

+1 hour

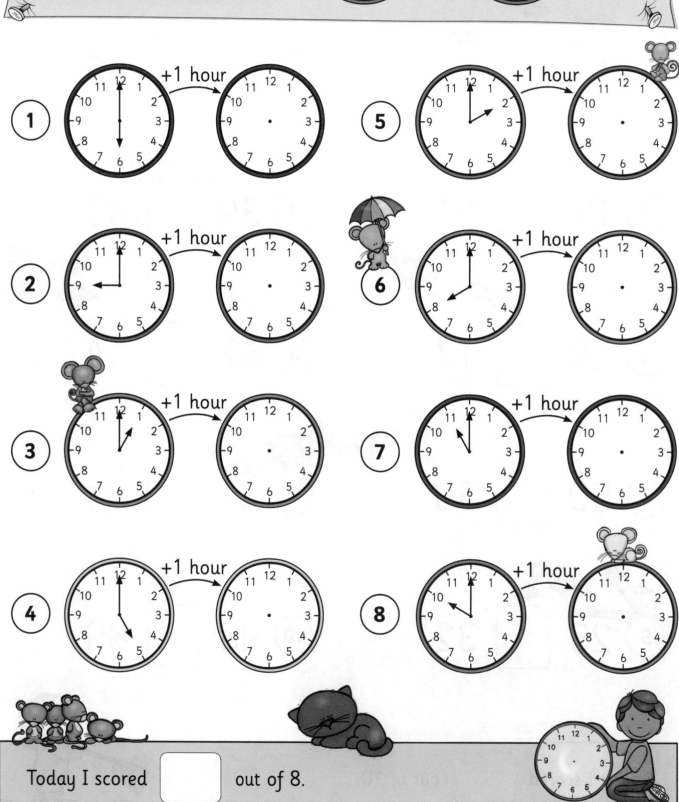

1 +1 hour

2 +1 hour

3 +1 hour

4 +1 hour

5 +1 hour

6 +1 hour

7 +1 hour

8 +1 hour

Today I scored ⬚ out of 8.

Week 5 — Day 1

Count in steps to find the missing numbers.

In steps of ten...

0   10   20   30   40

In steps of five...

1   0   5   10   15

In steps of two...

2   0   2   4   6

In steps of ten...

3   10   20   30   40

In steps of ten...

4   6   16   26   36

In steps of ten...

5   1   31   41   51

Today I scored ☐ out of 10.

Week 5 — Day 2

Write how much
water is in the jar
in litres or millilitres.

4 litres

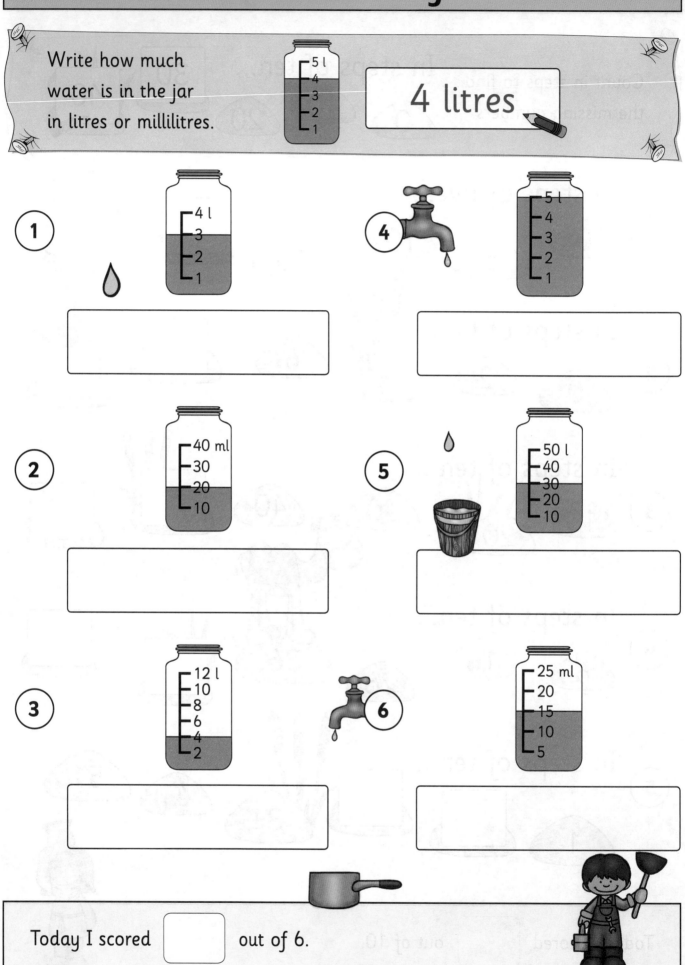

1

2

3

4

5

6

Today I scored [ ] out of 6.

Week 5 — Day 3

Estimate the numbers the arrows are pointing to.

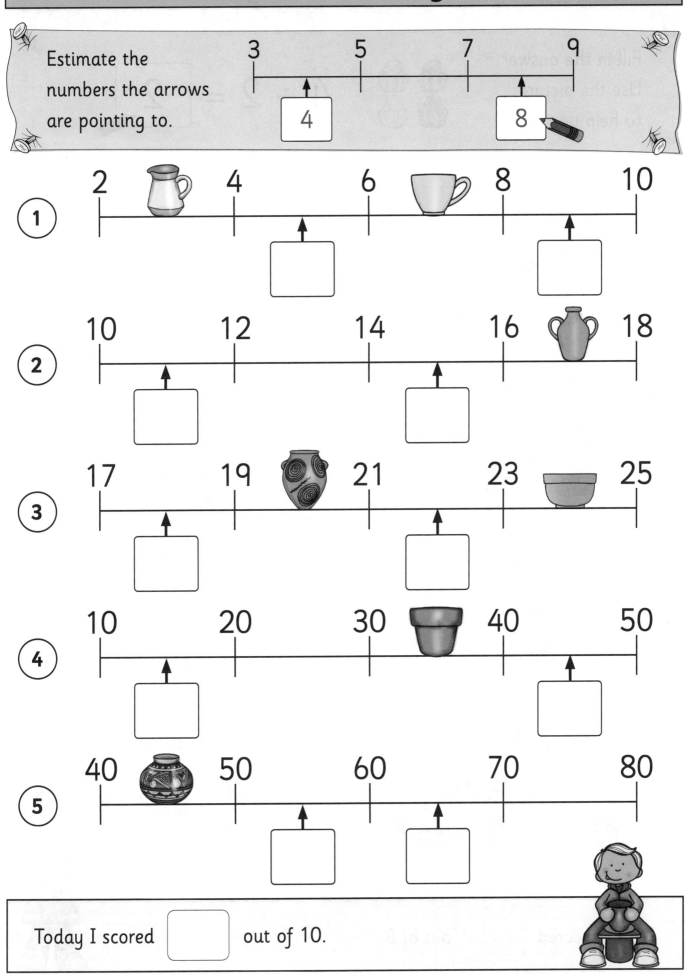

3　　5　　7　　9

4

8

1 | 2　　4　　6　　8　　10

2 | 10　　12　　14　　16　　18

3 | 17　　19　　21　　23　　25

4 | 10　　20　　30　　40　　50

5 | 40　　50　　60　　70　　80

Today I scored [　] out of 10.

　　　　Year 2 Maths — Autumn Term

Week 5 — Day 4

Fill in the answer.
Use the picture
to help you.

 $4 \div 2 = \boxed{2}$

(1) $2 \times 5 = \boxed{}$

(5) $2 \div 2 = \boxed{}$

(2) $10 \div 2 = \boxed{}$

(6) $8 \div 4 = \boxed{}$

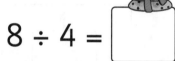

(3) $6 \div 2 = \boxed{}$

(7) $3 \times 5 = \boxed{}$

(4) $7 \times 2 = \boxed{}$

(8) $20 \div 5 = \boxed{}$

Today I scored $\boxed{}$ out of 8.

Year 2 Maths — Autumn Term

Week 5 — Day 5

 The objects on the left make the number 14. Each object represents a ten or a one. Fill in the missing number made by these objects.

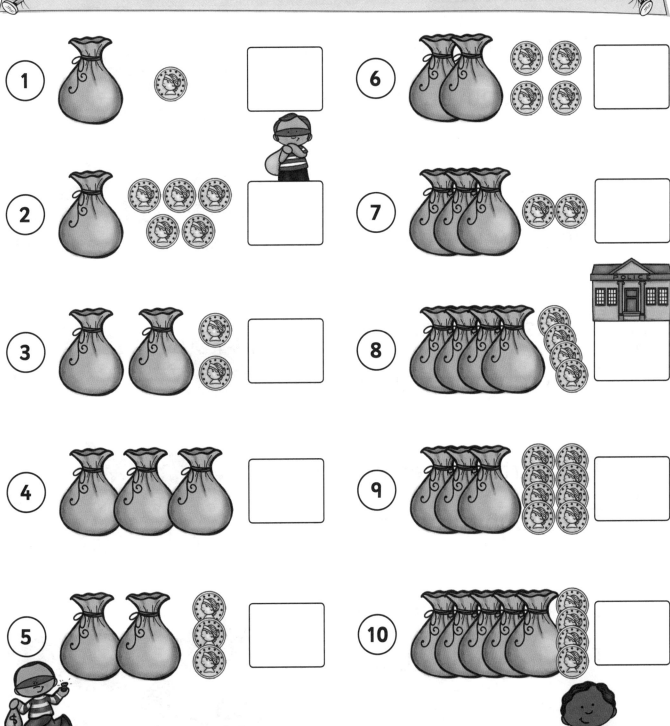

1

2

3

4

5

6

7

8

9

10

Today I scored [ ] out of 10.

Year 2 Maths — Autumn Term

Week 6 — Day 1

Look at the picture. Circle the right animals.

The beetle in front of the grass.

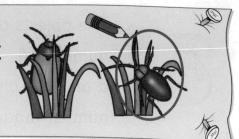

1. The frog behind the reeds.
   The fly above the reeds.

2. The fox on top of a bin.
   The crow in front of a bin.

3. The fish in front of a rock.
   The crab below a rock.

4. The butterfly behind a plant.
   The ladybird on top of a plant.

5. The otter on top of a log.
   The dragonfly above a log.

Today I scored [ ] out of 10.

Week 6 — Day 2

Fill in the answer.

15 + 10 = 25

(1) 24 + 3 = ☐

(6) 47 – 5 = ☐

(2) 17 + 2 = ☐

(7) 64 + 30 = ☐

(3) 95 – 1 = ☐

(8) 38 + 4 = ☐

(4) 49 – 8 = ☐

(9) 86 – 40 = ☐

(5) 32 + 20 = ☐

(10) 52 – 7 = ☐

Today I scored ☐ out of 10.

Year 2 Maths — Autumn Term

Week 6 — Day 3

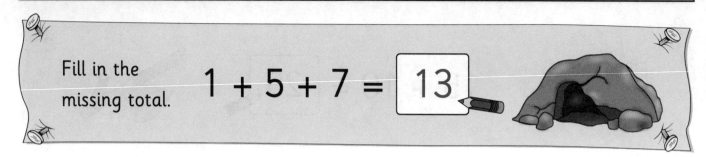

Fill in the missing total.

$$1 + 5 + 7 = \boxed{13}$$

(1) $4 + 3 + 1 = \boxed{}$

(6) $4 + 2 + 5 = \boxed{}$

(2) $7 + 2 + 3 = \boxed{}$

(7) $8 + 4 + 1 = \boxed{}$

(3) $3 + 9 + 6 = \boxed{}$

(8) $5 + 6 + 8 = \boxed{}$

(4) $2 + 8 + 7 = \boxed{}$

(9) $9 + 5 + 4 = \boxed{}$

(5) $1 + 3 + 9 = \boxed{}$

(10) $6 + 7 + 2 = \boxed{}$

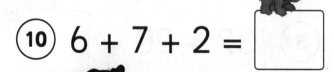

Today I scored $\boxed{}$ out of 10.

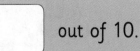

Year 2 Maths — Autumn Term

Week 6 — Day 4

Look at the pattern. Which number would be in the next red square?

9 10 11 12 13 14 | 17

1

1 2 3 4 5 6 7 8

2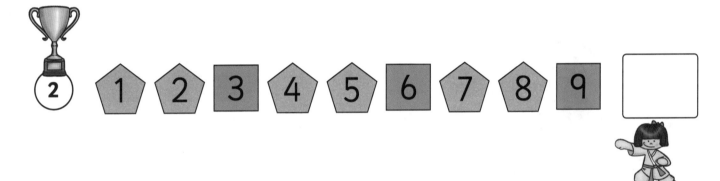

1 2 3 4 5 6 7 8 9

3

7 8 9 10 11 12 13 14

4

4 6 8 10 12 14 16 18

5

10 12 14 16 18 20 22 24 26

Today I scored [ ] out of 5.

Year 2 Maths — Autumn Term

Week 6 — Day 5

Draw a wall that is half as long as the wall shown.

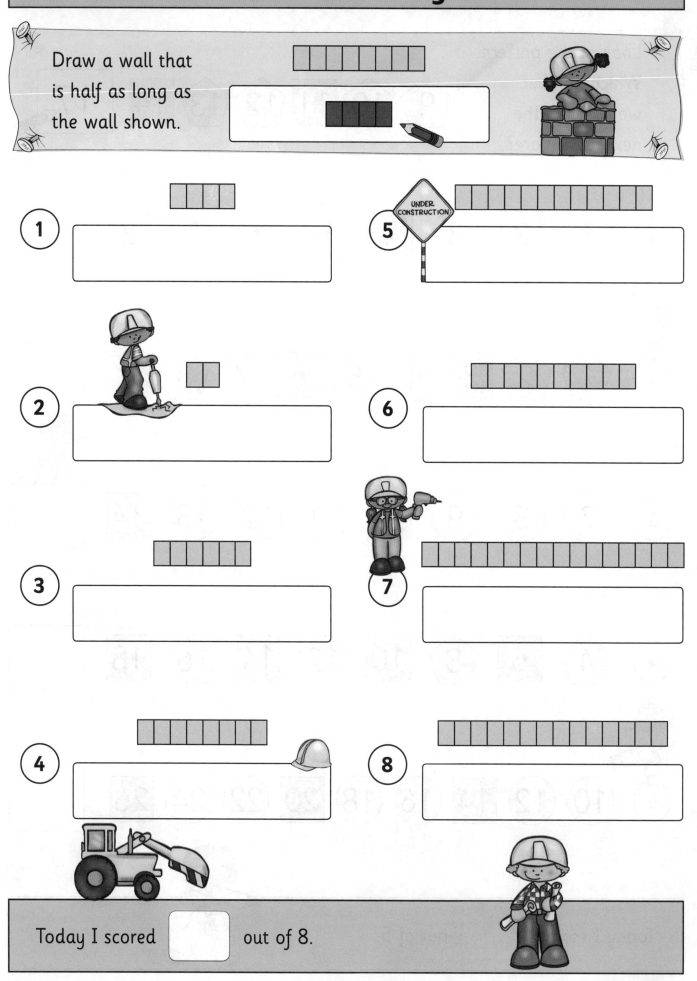

1

2

3

4

5

6

7

8

Today I scored ☐ out of 8.

Week 7 — Day 1

Tick the box if exactly
one quarter of the
shape is coloured in.

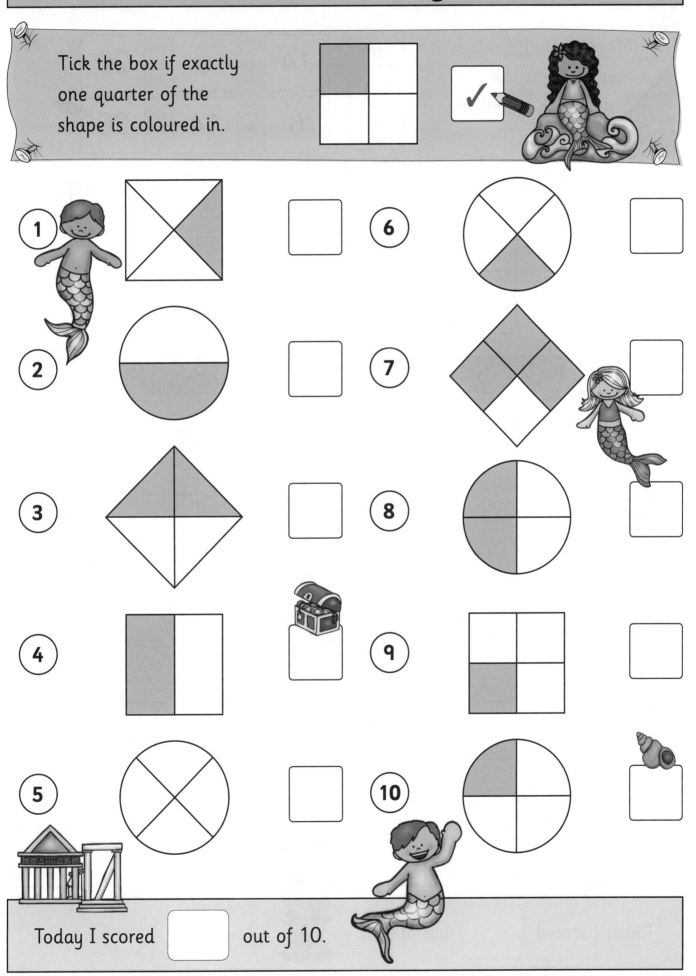

1

2

3

4

5

6

7

8

9

10

Today I scored ☐ out of 10.

Year 2 Maths — Autumn Term

Week 7 — Day 2

Make two different
number sentences.
Only use the numbers
in the box.

| 20 |
| 14 |
| 6 |

$$14 + 6 = 20$$

$$6 + 14 = 20$$

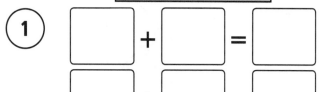

8 1 7

1

$$\boxed{} + \boxed{} = \boxed{}$$

$$\boxed{} + \boxed{} = \boxed{}$$

3 16 19

5

$$\boxed{} + \boxed{} = \boxed{}$$

$$\boxed{} + \boxed{} = \boxed{}$$

2 5 3

2

$$\boxed{} + \boxed{} = \boxed{}$$

$$\boxed{} + \boxed{} = \boxed{}$$

3 18 15

6

$$\boxed{} + \boxed{} = \boxed{}$$

$$\boxed{} + \boxed{} = \boxed{}$$

0 9 9

3

$$\boxed{} + \boxed{} = \boxed{}$$

$$\boxed{} + \boxed{} = \boxed{}$$

11 5 6

7

$$\boxed{} + \boxed{} = \boxed{}$$

$$\boxed{} + \boxed{} = \boxed{}$$

16 4 12

4

$$\boxed{} + \boxed{} = \boxed{}$$

$$\boxed{} + \boxed{} = \boxed{}$$

7 15 8

8

$$\boxed{} + \boxed{} = \boxed{}$$

$$\boxed{} + \boxed{} = \boxed{}$$

Today I scored $\boxed{}$ out of 8.

Week 7 — Day 3

Fill in the missing number.

$$40 + 60 = 100$$

1. $\boxed{} + 2 = 10$

2. $6 + \boxed{} = 10$

3. $30 + \boxed{} = 100$

4. $\boxed{} + 5 = 10$

5. $80 + \boxed{} = 100$

6. $\boxed{} + 1 = 10$

7. $7 + \boxed{} = 10$

8. $\boxed{} + 90 = 100$

9. $\boxed{} + 10 = 10$

10. $50 + \boxed{} = 100$

Today I scored $\boxed{}$ out of 10.

Year 2 Maths — Autumn Term

Week 7 — Day 4

Write the total amount of money.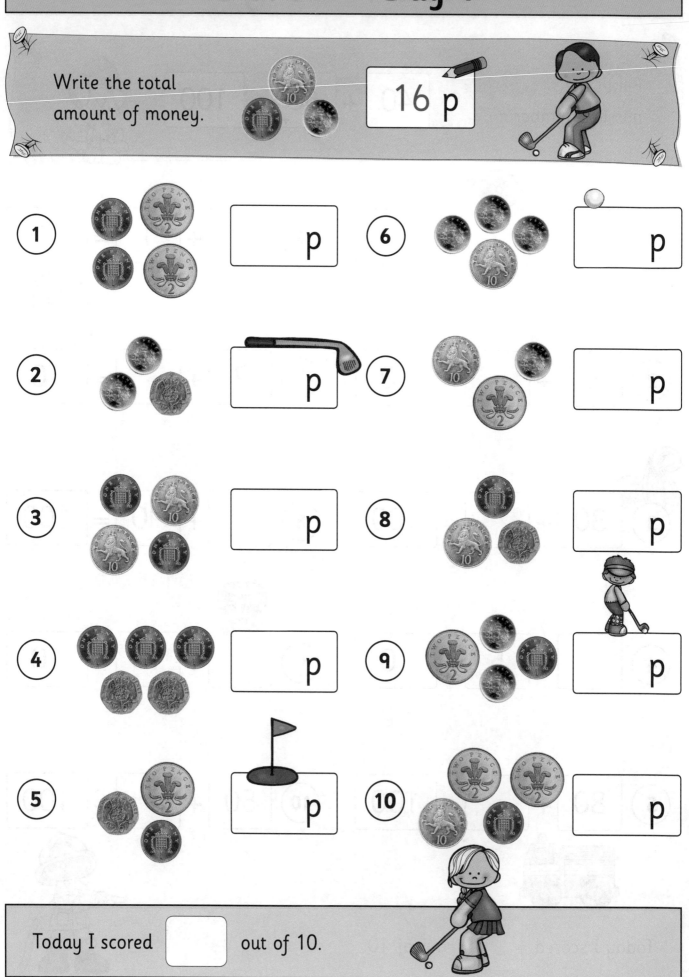

| 16 p |

1 _____ p

2 _____ p

3 _____ p

4 _____ p

5 _____ p

6 _____ p

7 _____ p

8 _____ p

9 _____ p

10 _____ p

Today I scored [   ] out of 10.

Week 7 — Day 5

These clocks show times in the afternoon. Tick the clock that shows the later time.

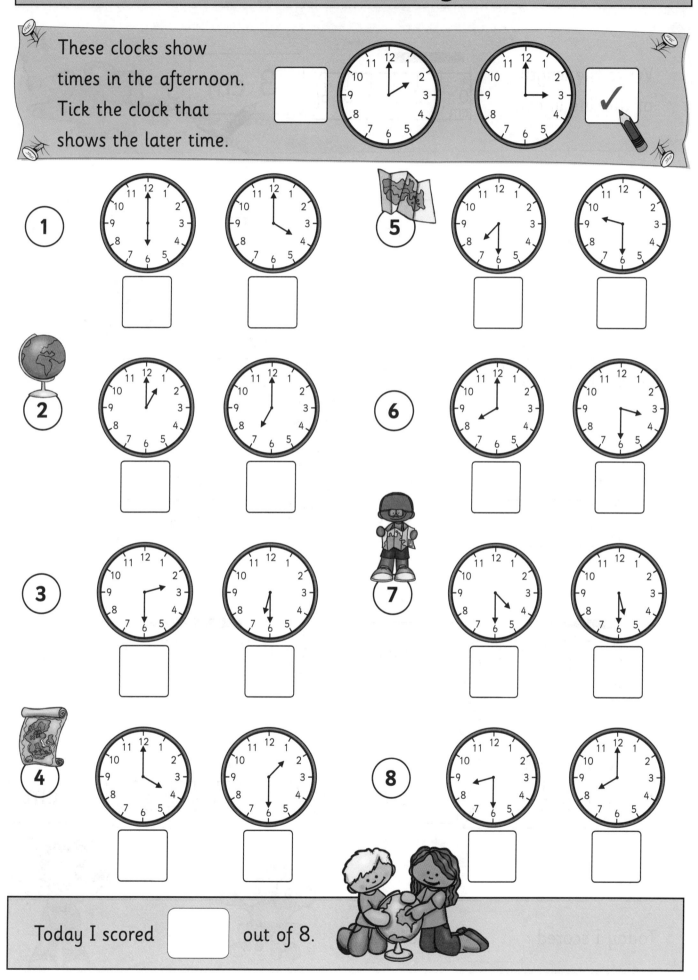

1

2

3

4

5

6

7

8

Today I scored [ ] out of 8.

Year 2 Maths — Autumn Term

Week 8 — Day 1

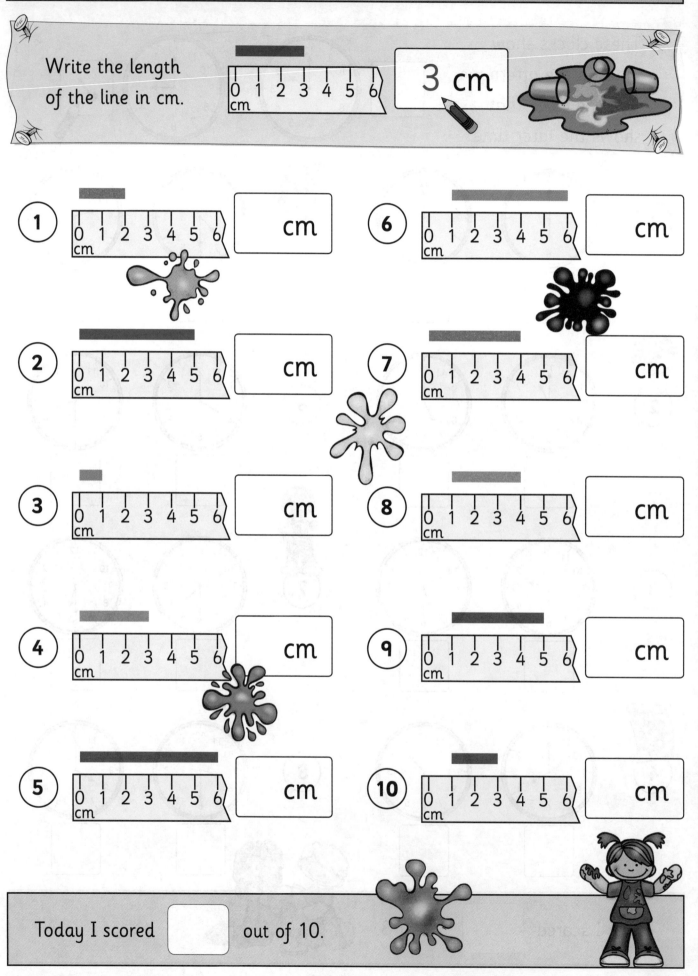

Write the length of the line in cm.

3 cm

1   cm

2   cm

3   cm

4   cm

5   cm

6   cm

7   cm

8   cm

9   cm

10   cm

Today I scored ☐ out of 10.

Week 8 — Day 2

Look at the clock.
Write the time
in words.

.......half past.......
.....ten...........

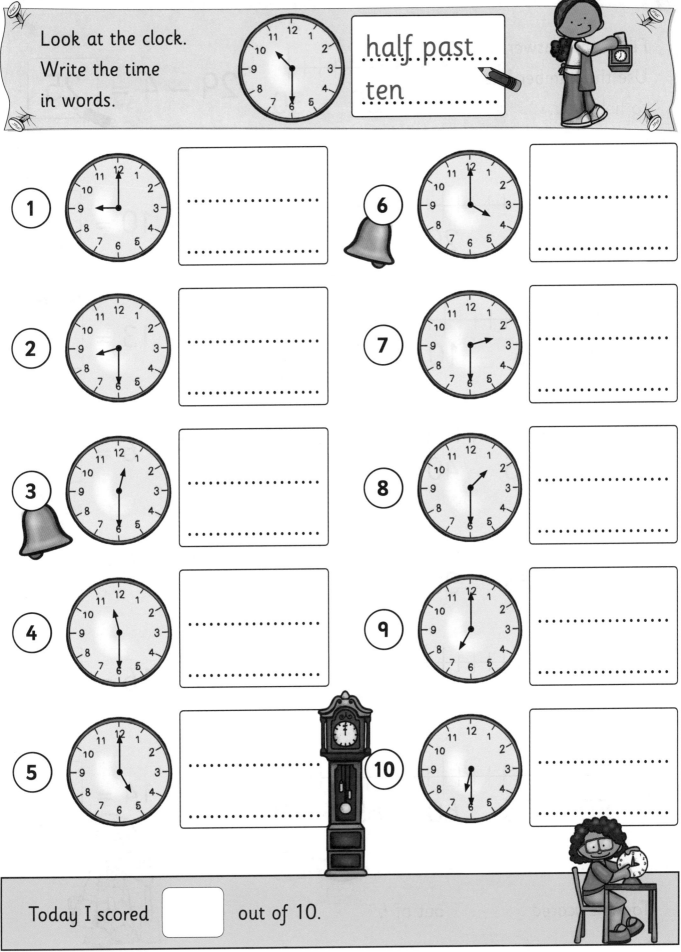

1

2

3

4

5

6

7

8

9

10

Today I scored ☐ out of 10.

Week 8 — Day 3

Fill in the answer.
Use the number line
to help you.

20　25　30

$29 - 4 =$ 　25

1
10　15　20　25　30

$12 + 10 =$ ☐

2
0　5　10　15　20

$3 + 13 =$ ☐

3
30　35　40　45　50

$43 - 6 =$ ☐

4
20　25　30　35　40

$39 - 18 =$ ☐

5
60　65　70　75　80

$61 + 16 =$ ☐

6
50　55　60　65　70

$70 - 14 =$ ☐

Today I scored ☐ out of 6.

Week 8 — Day 4

Use the picture to fill in the missing numbers.

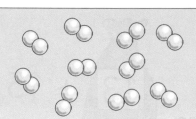

$$2 \times 10 = 20$$

1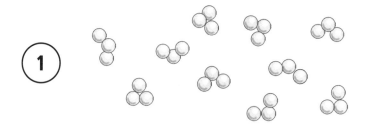

$$\boxed{} \times 10 = \boxed{}$$

2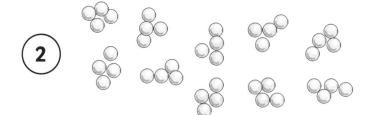

$$\boxed{} \times 10 = \boxed{}$$

3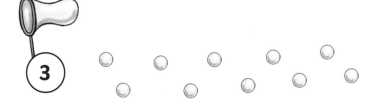

$$\boxed{} \times 10 = \boxed{}$$

4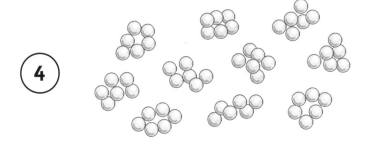

$$\boxed{} \times 10 = \boxed{}$$

5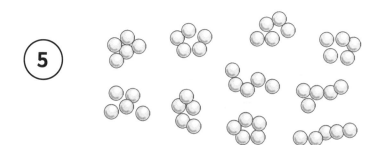

$$\boxed{} \times 10 = \boxed{}$$

Today I scored $\boxed{}$ out of 10.

Year 2 Maths — Autumn Term

Week 8 — Day 5

The number of marbles
in the bag is shown.
Some more marbles are added.
Write the total amount in the bag.

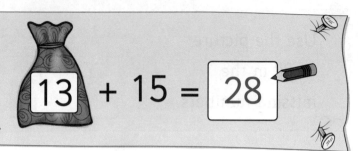

$13 + 15 = 28$

1. $10 + 16 = \boxed{}$

2. $23 + 14 = \boxed{}$

3. $21 + 13 = \boxed{}$

4. $22 + 55 = \boxed{}$

5. $31 + 11 = \boxed{}$

6. $16 + 22 = \boxed{}$

7. $26 + 25 = \boxed{}$

8. $36 + 41 = \boxed{}$

9. $17 + 29 = \boxed{}$

10. $35 + 47 = \boxed{}$

Today I scored $\boxed{}$ out of 10.

Week 9 — Day 1

Colour in the shape to show the right amount.

a half

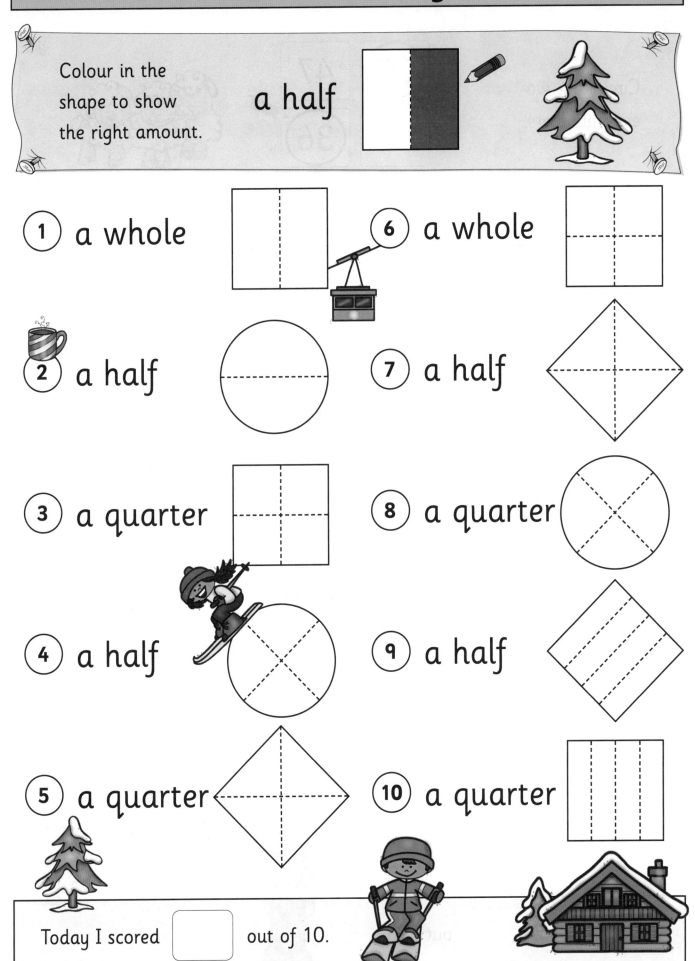

1. a whole

2. a half

3. a quarter

4. a half

5. a quarter

6. a whole

7. a half

8. a quarter

9. a half

10. a quarter

Today I scored [ ] out of 10.

Year 2 Maths — Autumn Term

Week 9 — Day 2

Circle the two even numbers.

⟨20⟩	47
5	⟨36⟩

1

35	4
19	58

5

74	28
21	3

2

75	66
24	11

6

42	7
8	53

3

89	37
90	46

7

2	70
93	17

4

39	82
12	73

8

97	51
14	86

Today I scored ☐ out of 8.

Week 9 — Day 3

Draw where the arrow points after the turn. 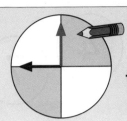 A quarter turn clockwise

1  A half turn

5 A quarter turn anticlockwise

2 A quarter turn clockwise

6 A half turn

3 A quarter turn anticlockwise

7 A three-quarter turn clockwise

4 A three-quarter turn clockwise

8 A three-quarter turn anticlockwise

Today I scored ☐ out of 8.

Year 2 Maths — Autumn Term

Week 9 — Day 4

Count in steps of three to fill in the missing numbers.

1 0   3   6   9 ☐ ☐

2 33 36 39 42 ☐ ☐

3 15 18 21 24 ☐ ☐

4 2 5 8 11 ☐ ☐

5 10 13 16 19 ☐ ☐

Today I scored ☐ out of 10.

Week 9 — Day 5

Work out the answer.

$3 \times 10 = \boxed{30}$

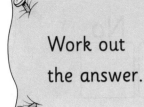

1. $8 \times 2 = \boxed{}$

6. $4 \times 5 = \boxed{}$

2. $9 \times 10 = \boxed{}$

7. $7 \times 10 = \boxed{}$

3. $3 \times 2 = \boxed{}$

8. $7 \times 2 = \boxed{}$

4. $5 \times 10 = \boxed{}$

9. $4 \times 10 = \boxed{}$

5. $2 \times 5 = \boxed{}$

10. $7 \times 5 = \boxed{}$

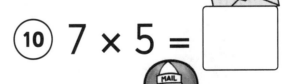

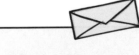

Today I scored $\boxed{}$ out of 10.

Year 2 Maths — Autumn Term

Week 10 — Day 1

Does the word match the shape?
Tick the right box.

cube  Yes No ✓

1 pyramid Yes No

2 sphere Yes No

3 cube Yes No

4 cuboid  Yes No

5 pyramid Yes No

6 cube 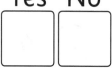 Yes No

7 pyramid Yes No

8 sphere 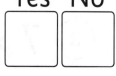 Yes No

9 cuboid 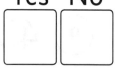 Yes No

10 sphere  Yes No

Today I scored ☐ out of 10.

Week 10 — Day 2

Complete the multiplication number sentence.

$2 \times 3 = 3 \times \boxed{2}$

(1) $3 \times 10 = \boxed{} \times 3$

(6) $10 \times \boxed{} = 2 \times 10$

(2) $10 \times \boxed{} = 5 \times 10$

(7) $1 \times 2 = 2 \times \boxed{}$

(3) $\boxed{} \times 2 = 2 \times 5$

(8) $3 \times \boxed{} = 5 \times 3$

(4) $2 \times 4 = 4 \times \boxed{}$

(9) $\boxed{} \times 5 = 5 \times 1$

(5) $10 \times \boxed{} = 8 \times 10$

(10) $5 \times 4 = \boxed{} \times 5$

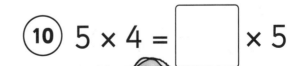

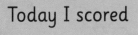 Today I scored $\boxed{}$ out of 10.

Year 2 Maths — Autumn Term

Week 10 — Day 3

Count backwards in steps of 10 from the number in the egg.
Circle the two numbers that you say.

20 | (10) | 5 | (0)

① 30 | 20 | 15 | 10

⑥ 35 | 45 | 25 | 15

② 25 | 15 | 10 | 5

⑦ 60 | 40 | 35 | 30

③ 40 | 30 | 20 | 15

⑧ 45 | 30 | 25 | 15

④ 50 | 60 | 40 | 30

⑨ 55 | 45 | 25 | 10

⑤ 70 | 65 | 60 | 50

⑩ 65 | 55 | 35 | 0

Today I scored ☐ out of 10.

Week 10 — Day 4

Write × or ÷ to complete the number sentence.

2 × 4 = 8

1 10 ☐ 2 = 20

2 3 ☐ 5 = 15

3 25 = 5 ☐ 5

4 50 = 5 ☐ 10

5 10 ☐ 2 = 5

6 60 = 10 ☐ 6

7 40 ☐ 4 = 10

8 8 = 40 ☐ 5

9 5 ☐ 9 = 45

10 7 = 35 ☐ 5

Today I scored ☐ out of 10.

Year 2 Maths — Autumn Term

Week 10 — Day 5

Circle 3 equal groups. Use the groups to fill in the answer.

 $6 \div 3 =$ **2**

(1)  $3 \div 3 =$ [ ]

(2) 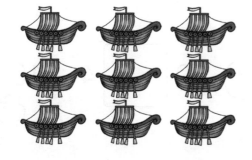 $9 \div 3 =$ [ ]

(3)  $15 \div 3 =$ [ ]

(4)  $12 \div 3 =$ [ ]

(5)  $18 \div 3 =$ [ ]

Today I scored [ ] out of 10.

Week 11 — Day 1

Circle the amount with the same value as the coins.

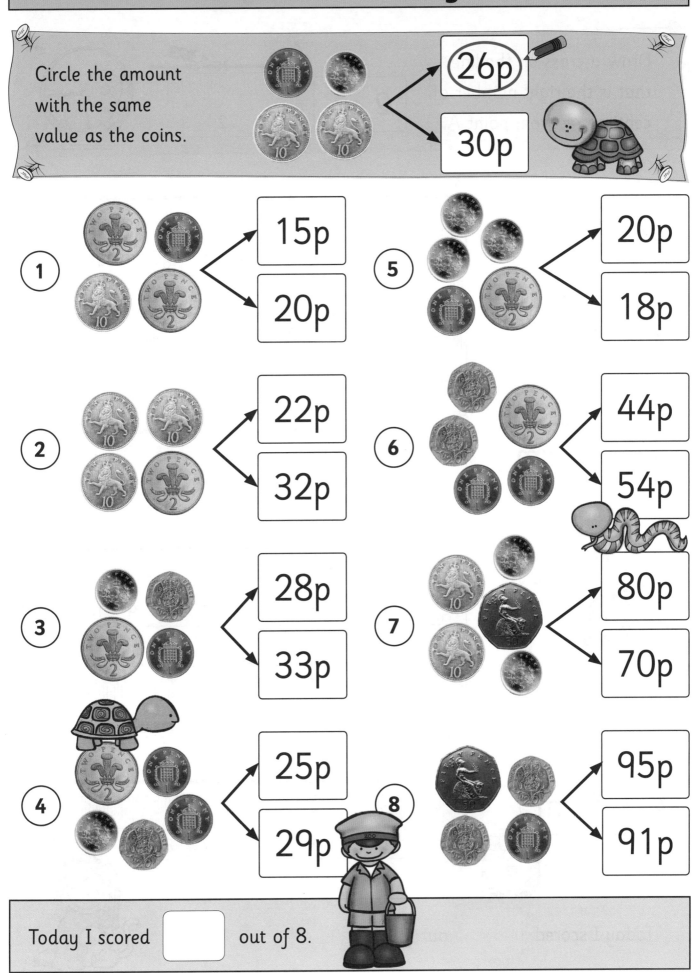

Week 11 — Day 2

Draw a cross on the line that is the right number of centimetres from point A.

2 cm

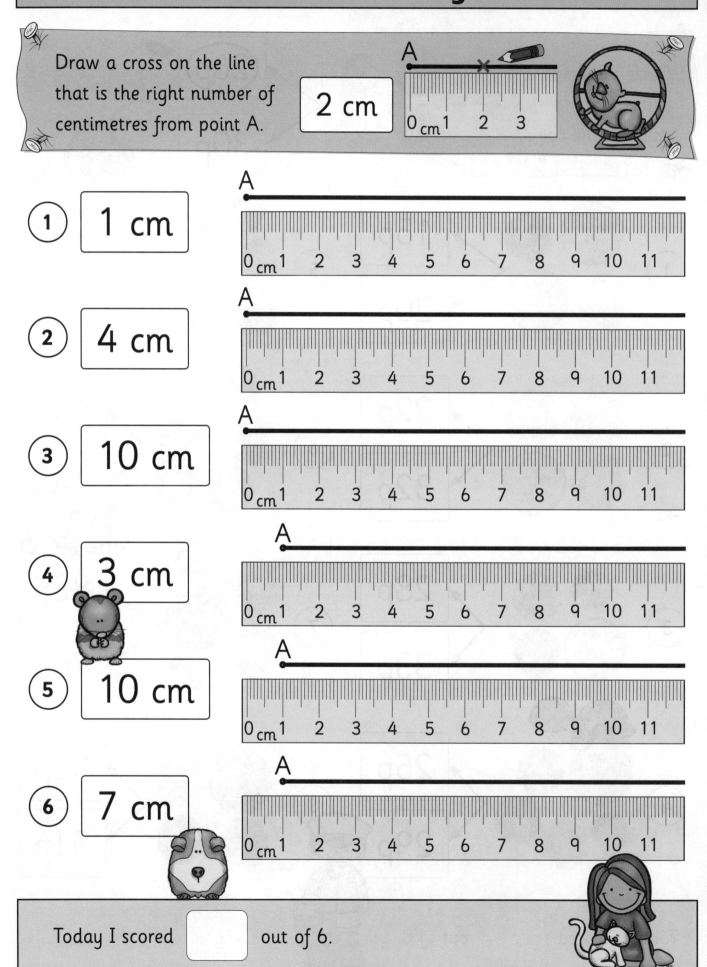

1) 1 cm

2) 4 cm

3) 10 cm

4) 3 cm

5) 10 cm

6) 7 cm

Today I scored ☐ out of 6.

Week 11 — Day 3

Fill in the missing number.

$$20 - 5 = 15$$

(1) $20 - 10 = \boxed{}$

(6) $\boxed{} - 9 = 31$

(2) $20 - \boxed{} = 5$

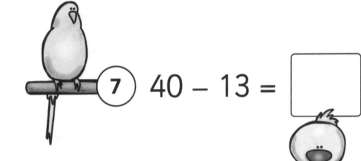

(7) $40 - 13 = \boxed{}$

(3) $\boxed{} - 0 = 10$

(8) $20 - \boxed{} = 3$

(4) $20 - 16 = \boxed{}$

(9) $30 - \boxed{} = 18$

(5) $30 - 8 = \boxed{}$

(10) $40 - \boxed{} = 17$

Today I scored $\boxed{}$ out of 10.

Year 2 Maths — Autumn Term

Week 11 — Day 4

Circle two coins that add to make the amount shown in the box.

10p

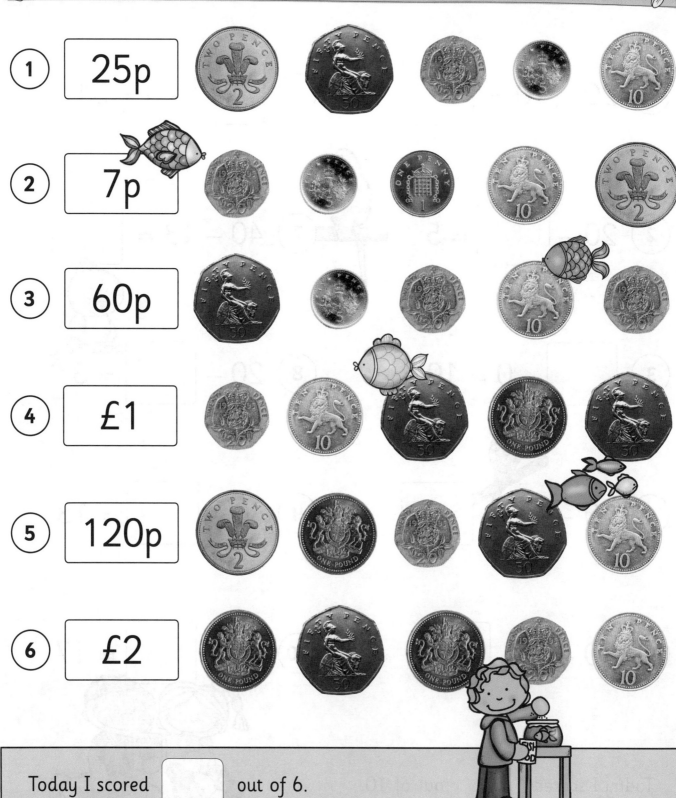

1 25p

2 7p

3 60p

4 £1

5 120p

6 £2

Today I scored ☐ out of 6.

Week 11 — Day 5

Look at the jar of sweets. Fill in the missing number.

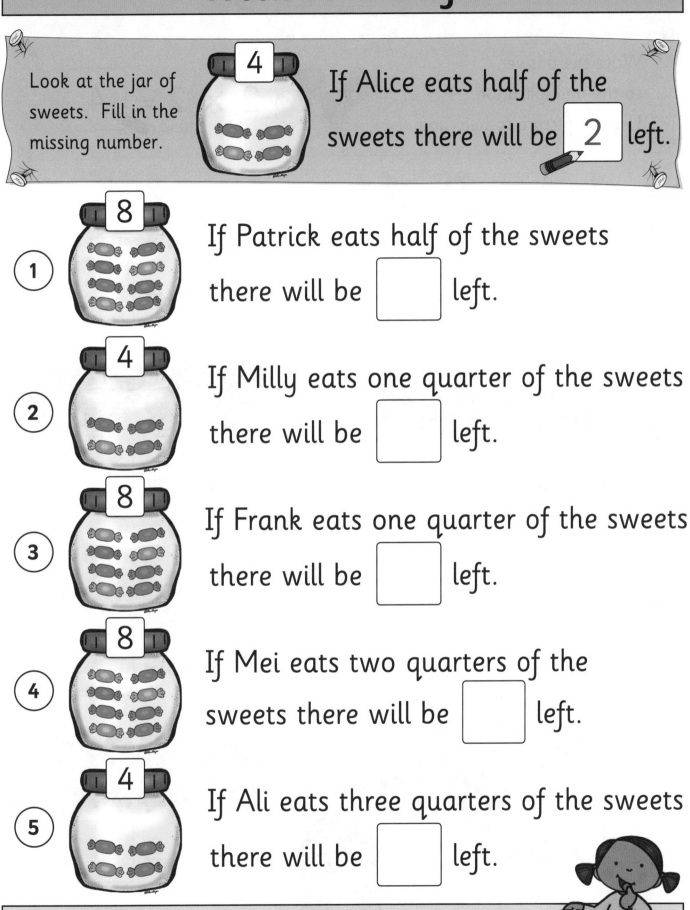

4

If Alice eats half of the sweets there will be **2** left.

1 **8** If Patrick eats half of the sweets there will be ☐ left.

2 **4** If Milly eats one quarter of the sweets there will be ☐ left.

3 **8** If Frank eats one quarter of the sweets there will be ☐ left.

4 **8** If Mei eats two quarters of the sweets there will be ☐ left.

5 **4** If Ali eats three quarters of the sweets there will be ☐ left.

Today I scored ☐ out of 5.

Year 2 Maths — Autumn Term

Week 12 — Day 1

Write the answer
to the multiplication.
Use the picture to help you.

 $2 \times 2 = \boxed{4}$

 (1)

$2 \times 3 = \boxed{}$

(5)

$5 \times 3 = \boxed{}$

(2)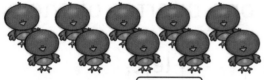

$5 \times 2 = \boxed{}$

(6)

$2 \times 4 = \boxed{}$

(3)

$7 \times 2 = \boxed{}$

 (7)

$5 \times 4 = \boxed{}$

(4)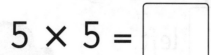

$5 \times 5 = \boxed{}$

(8)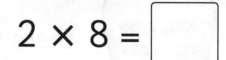

$2 \times 8 = \boxed{}$

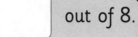

Today I scored $\boxed{}$ out of 8.

Year 2 Maths — Autumn Term

Week 12 — Day 2

Read the description. Write the day of the week that the music lesson is on.

Today is Wednesday. My lesson is tomorrow.

Thursday

1 Today is Monday.

My lesson is tomorrow.

2 Tomorrow is Tuesday.

My lesson is today.

3 Yesterday was Thursday.

My lesson is tomorrow.

4 Tomorrow is Sunday.

My lesson was yesterday.

5 Yesterday was Saturday.

My lesson is tomorrow.

Today I scored [ ] out of 5.

Year 2 Maths — Autumn Term

Week 12 — Day 3

How much more does the first toy cost than the second toy?

20p 10p 10p

1 30p 10p ____ p

5 40p 30p ____ p

2 30p 20p ____ p

6 50p 35p ____ p

3 30p 15p ____ p

7 45p 10p ____ p

4 40p 20p ____ p

8 45p 40p ____ p

Today I scored ____ out of 8.

Week 12 — Day 4

Isaac buys a present for 22p.
Will he get any change from the
coins shown? Tick the right box.

Yes No

☐ ✓

1 Yes No ☐ ☐

2 Yes No ☐ ☐

3 Yes No ☐ ☐

4 Yes No ☐ ☐

5 Yes No ☐ ☐

6 Yes No ☐ ☐

7 Yes No ☐ ☐

8 Yes No ☐ ☐

9 Yes No ☐ ☐

10 Yes No ☐ ☐

Today I scored ☐ out of 10.

Year 2 Maths — Autumn Term

Week 12 — Day 5

Write the total cost of the items.
Julia pays for the items
with a 50p coin.
Circle the coin she gets as change.

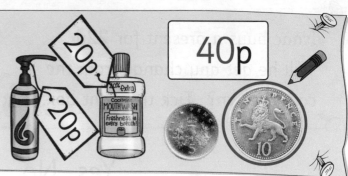

40p

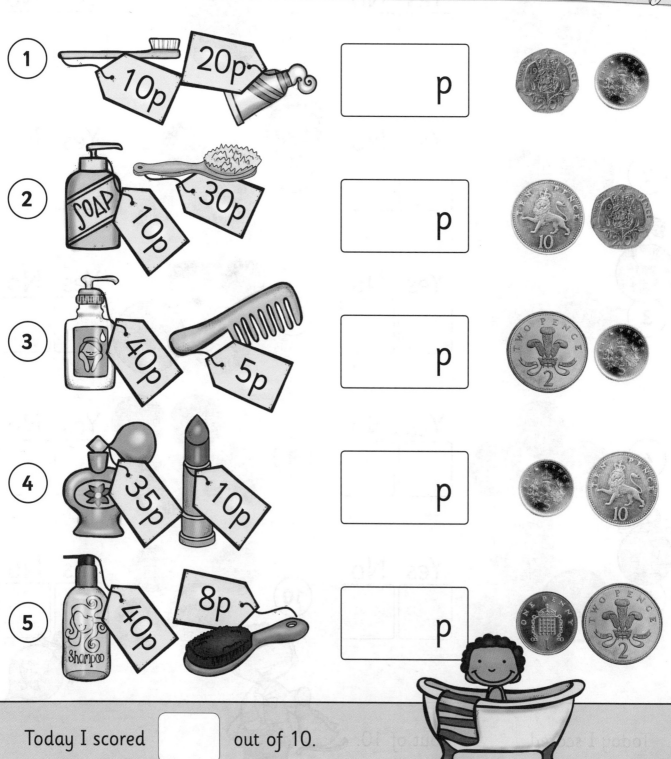

(1) 10p 20p _____ p

(2) SOAP 10p 30p _____ p

(3) 40p 5p _____ p

(4) 35p 10p _____ p

(5) Shampoo 40p 8p _____ p

Today I scored [ ] out of 10.